Beautiful me HAIR

SALON

PLEASE
RETURN TO
404) 732-2965
404) 3²⁰ or 20-6889

INSPIRE

HAIR FASHION FOR SALON CLIENTS

**Ladies & Gentleman
Salon & Spa**
HAIR: Jennifer Juratovac
COLOR: Sal Misseri
PHOTO: Tom Carson

Table of Contents Volume 77

Tangles Salon
HAIR: Michelle Azouz
MAKEUP: Betty Mckonnen
PHOTO: Tom Carson

Attitudes A Salon
HAIR: Kristie Laytart
PHOTO: Tom Carson

Attitudes A Salon
HAIR: Janice Edinger
MAKEUP: Kim Bowers
PHOTO: Tom Carson

Casal Aveda Institute
HAIR: Tracy Thomas
PHOTO: Tom Carson

Casal Aveda Institute
HAIR: April Zehner
PHOTO: Tom Carson

Stilo Salon of San Mateo
HAIR: Victoria Pelaez-Pintal & Maria Montilla
COLOR: Victoria Pelaez-Pintal
MAKEUP: Victoria Pelaez-Pintal
PHOTO: Taggart Winterhalter
for Purely Visual

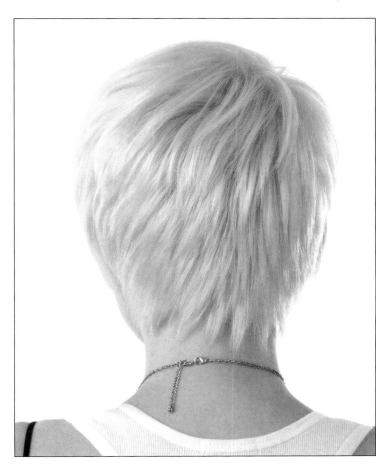

Attitudes A Salon
HAIR: Tanya Lange
MAKEUP: Kim Bowers
PHOTO: Tom Carson

Kenneth Shuler
Schools of
Cosmetology
HAIR: Tonya Dalton
PHOTO: Tom Carson

Sheer Professionals Salon
HAIR: Melissa Lipaj
PHOTO: Tom Carson

**Vanis Salon &
Day Spa**
HAIR: Jeremy Dowling
MAKEUP: Jennifer Donelson
PHOTO: Tom Carson

Stilo Salon of San Mateo
HAIR: Mia Helms & Elaine Nicdao
COLOR: Mia Helms
MAKEUP: Victoria Pelaez-Pintal
PHOTO: Taggart Winterhalter
for Purely Visual

Kenneth Shuler
Schools of Cosmetology
HAIR: Jessica Rhyne
PHOTO: Tom Carson

Diadema Hair Fashion
HAIR: Diadema
MAKEUP: Sara Mencattelli per "2001 Milano"
PHOTO: Stefano Bidini

Vanis Salon & Day Spa
HAIR: Brooklyn Badten
MAKEUP: Natalie Rubio
PHOTO: Tom Carson

Attitudes A Salon
HAIR: Jill Nijakowski
PHOTO: Tom Carson

**Attitudes
A Salon**
HAIR: Felicia Gonzales/
Kim Bowers
PHOTO: Tom Carson

Attitudes A Salon
HAIR: Holly Tedrick
PHOTO: Tom Carson

Attitudes A Salon
HAIR: Janice Edinger
COLOR: Chelse Tucker
MAKEUP: Kim Bowers
PHOTO: Tom Carson

Dimensions Hair Studio for Shear Express Inc.
HAIR: Heather LeBouf
COLOR: Heather LeBouf
MAKEUP: Heather LeBouf
PHOTO: Wendy Reynolds

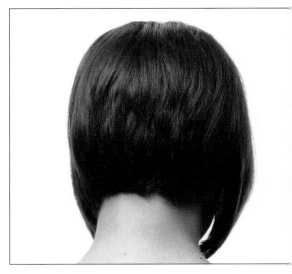

PON International
HAIR: Sara Wayne
MAKEUP: Sara Wayne
PHOTO: Taggart Winterhalter for Purely Visual

Currie Hair Skin & Nail Salon
HAIR: Nicky DeAngelo
MAKEUP: Nicky DeAngelo
PHOTO: Tom Carson

Casal Aveda Institute
HAIR: Rachel Parnell
PHOTO: Tom Carson

Kenneth Shuler Schools of Cosmetology
HAIR: Alicia Powell
PHOTO: Tom Carson

Sheer Professionals Salon
HAIR: Stephanie Snyder
PHOTO: Tom Carson

**Ladies & Gentlemen
Salon & Spa**
HAIR: Robin Schnell
COLOR: Sal Misseri
MAKEUP:
Lauren Remnick
PHOTO:
Tom Carson

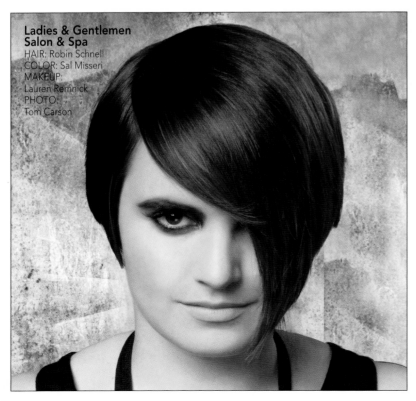

Casal Aveda Institute
HAIR: Kellie Shope
PHOTO: Tom Carson

Diadema Hair Fashion
HAIR: Diadema
MAKEUP: Sara Mencattelli
per "2001 Milano"
PHOTO: Stefano Bidini

Currie Hair Skin & Nail Salon
HAIR: Kristin Degnars
MAKEUP: Kristin Degnars
PHOTO: Tom Carson

Stilo Salon of San Mateo
HAIR: Mia Helms & Leigh Lee
COLOR: Mia Helms
MAKEUP: Victoria Pelaez-Pintal
PHOTO: Taggart Winterhalter
for Purely Visual

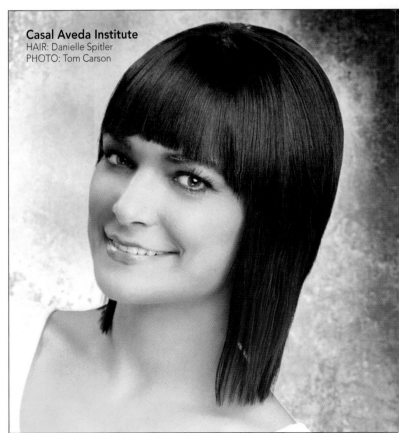

Casal Aveda Institute
HAIR: Danielle Spitler
PHOTO: Tom Carson

Pivot Point International
HAIR: Jens Hagenmüller,
Mina Lim & Joakim Roos
MAKEUP: Amy Howard
PHOTO: David Placek

**Pivot Point
International**
HAIR: Jens Hagenmüller,
Mina Lim & Joakim Roos
MAKEUP: Amy Howard
PHOTO: David Placek

Cloud 9 Salon
HAIR: Jerry Oliver
MAKEUP: Angie Mamone
PHOTO: Tom Carson

Cloud 9 Salon
HAIR: Danielle Ayers
MAKEUP: Jeni Pozell
PHOTO: Tom Carson

24

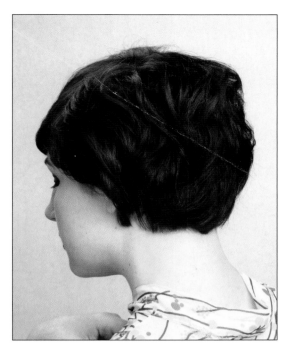

Kathy Adams Salon
HAIR: Nicki Hodges
MAKEUP: Ergene Tew
PHOTO: Tom Carson

Sheer Professionals Salon
HAIR: Jessica Raines
PHOTO: Tom Carson

The Brown Aveda Institute
HAIR: Tracie Sell
PHOTO: Tom Carson

Kathy Adams Salon
HAIR: Stephanie Adams
PHOTO: Tom Carson

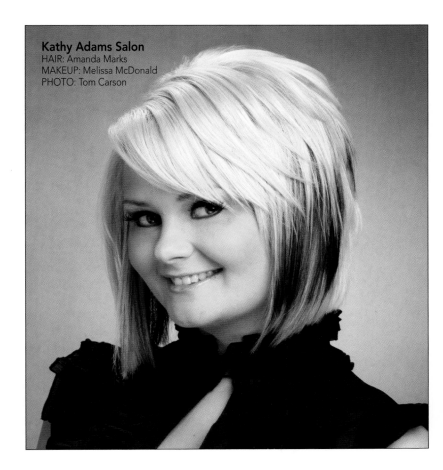

Kathy Adams Salon
HAIR: Amanda Marks
MAKEUP: Melissa McDonald
PHOTO: Tom Carson

Stilo Salon of San Mateo
HAIR: Victoria Pelaez-Pintal & Sabah Munayer
COLOR: Victoria Pelaez-Pintal
MAKEUP: Amber Skinner
PHOTO: Taggart Winterhalter
for Purely Visual

Stilo Salon of San Mateo
HAIR: Piera Rivasplata
MAKEUP: Amber Skinner
PHOTO: Taggart Winterhalter
for Purely Visual

Stilo Salon of San Mateo
HAIR: Samira Bakhtiary
MAKEUP: Amber Skinner
PHOTO: Taggart Winterhalter
for Purely Visual

Stilo Salon of San Mateo
HAIR: Mia Helms & Sabah Munayer
COLOR: Mia Helms
MAKEUP: Victoria Pelaez-Pintal
PHOTO: Taggart Winterhalter
for Purely Visual

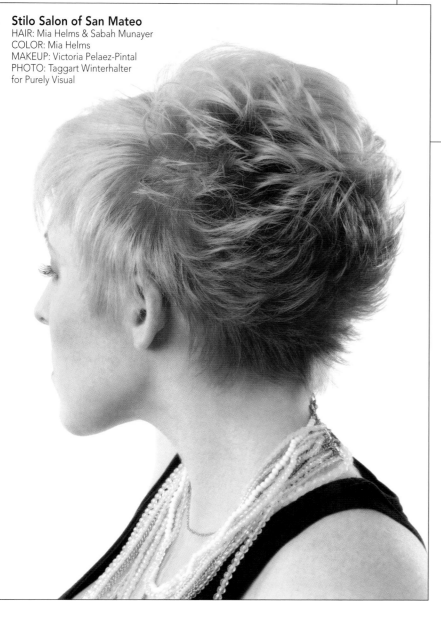

Pivot Point International
HAIR: Mina Lim
MAKEUP: Amy Howard
PHOTO: David Placek

**Kenneth Shuler
Schools of Cosmetology**
HAIR: Kim Crawford-Murphy
PHOTO: Tom Carson

Von Kekel Aveda Salon Spa
HAIR: Genevieve Wall
PHOTO: Tom Carson

Attitudes A Salon
HAIR: Tanya Lange
MAKEUP: Kristen King
PHOTO: Tom Carson

Attitudes A Salon
HAIR: Alexa Bly
PHOTO: Tom Carson

32

Kenneth Shuler
Schools of Cosmetology
HAIR: Tiffany Tennant
PHOTO: Tom Carson

Kenneth Shuler
Schools of Cosmetology
HAIR: Cana Dunlap
PHOTO: Tom Carson

The Brown Aveda Institute
HAIR: Amanda Buccilli
PHOTO: Tom Carson

Sheer Professionals Salon
HAIR: Donna Beam
PHOTO: Tom Carson

Kathy Adams Salon
HAIR: Cindy Freeze
MAKEUP: Melissa McDonald
PHOTO: Tom Carson

**The Ohio Academy
Paul Mitchell Partner
School**
HAIR: Cassandra Phipps
MAKEUP: Cassandra Phipps
PHOTO: Tom Carson

Sheer Professionals Salon
HAIR: Alison Burkhart
PHOTO: Tom Carson

Sheer Professionals Salon
HAIR: Jennifer Tennant
PHOTO: Tom Carson

36

Diadema Hair Fashion
HAIR: Diadema
MAKEUP: Sara Mencattelli
per "2001 Milano"
PHOTO: Stefano Bidini

Kathy Adams Salon
HAIR: Dalia Ardeu
MAKEUP: Autumn McCann
PHOTO: Tom Carson

Von Kekel Aveda Salon Spa
HAIR: Donna Arcangeli
PHOTO: Tom Carson

Ladies & Gentlemen Salon & Spa
HAIR: Holly Brown & Stacy Aquilla
COLOR: Sal Misseri
MAKEUP: Jodi Keeney
PHOTO: Tom Carson

American Beauty Academy
HAIR: Cassidy Wood
COLOR: Cassidy Wood
MAKEUP: Cassidy Wood
PHOTO: Joe Putnam

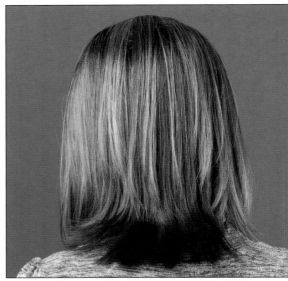

Dimensions Hair Studio
for Shear Express Inc.
HAIR: Kaylee Parrish
COLOR: Kaylee Parrish
MAKEUP:
Kaylee Parrish
PHOTO:
Wendy Reynolds

Ladies & Gentlemen Salon & Spa
HAIR: Robin Schnell
COLOR: Sal Misseri
MAKEUP: Lauren Remnick
PHOTO: Tom Carson

Attitudes A Salon
HAIR: Chelse Tucker
MAKEUP: Kim Bowers
PHOTO: Tom Carson

PON International
HAIR: Pon Saradeth
MAKEUP: Jamie Queenin
PHOTO: Taggart
Winterhalter
for Purely Visual

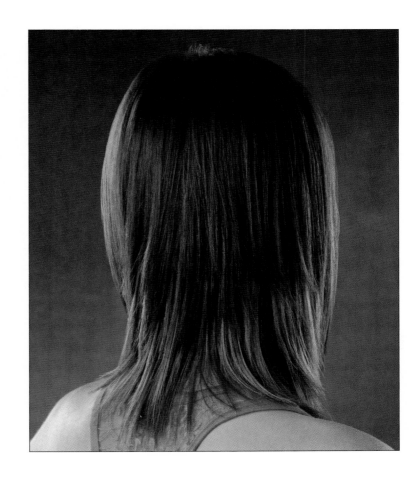

Claiborne's Salon
HAIR: Claiborne's Design Team
MAKEUP: Claiborne's
Design Team
PHOTO: Andy Allen

Sheer Professionals Salon
HAIR: Taylor Brenner
PHOTO: Tom Carson

Casal Aveda Institute
HAIR: Hannah Dorn
PHOTO: Tom Carson

Claiborne's Salon
HAIR: Claiborne's Design Team
MAKEUP: Claiborne's Design Team
PHOTO: Andy Allen

American Beauty Academy
HAIR: Chase Hargis
COLOR: Chase Hargis
MAKEUP: Chase Hargis
PHOTO: Joe Putnam

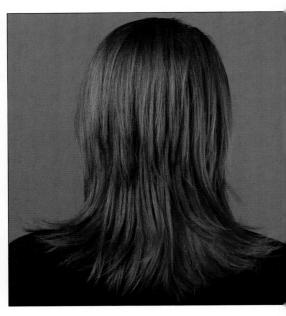

Attitudes A Salon
HAIR: Rosa Sutphin
MAKEUP: Rosa Sutphin
PHOTO: Tom Carson

PON International
HAIR: Sara Wayne
MAKEUP: Sara Wayne
PHOTO: Taggart Winterhalter
for Purely Visual

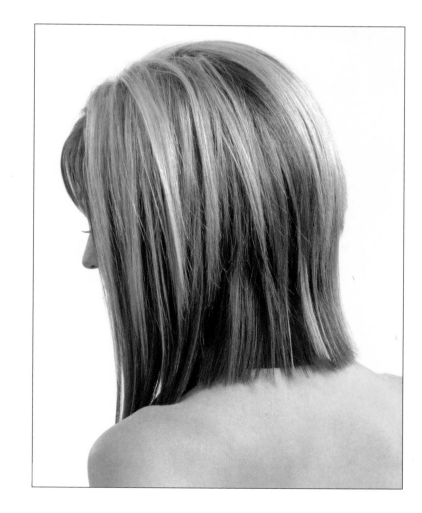

Salon Stile
HAIR: Paige Lemert
MAKEUP: Sophia Taylor
PHOTO: Tom Carson

Kenneth's Studio for Hair
HAIR: Ken Smith
MAKEUP: Yen Mai & Dan Forest
of Beverly Hills One of Alexandria
PHOTO: Tom Carson

**The Ohio Academy
Paul Mitchell Partner School**
HAIR: Elyse Jenkins
MAKEUP: Elyse Jenkins
PHOTO: Tom Carson

Von Kekel Aveda Salon Spa
HAIR: Ana Banda
PHOTO: Tom Carson

Casal Aveda Institute
HAIR: Gianna Nolfi
PHOTO: Tom Carson

**Currie Hair Skin &
Nail Salon**
HAIR: Jeremy Matthews
MAKEUP: Jess Moss
PHOTO: Tom Carson

Tangles Salon
HAIR: Leslie Cook
MAKEUP: Betty Mckonnen
PHOTO: Tom Carson

LONG STYLES

Casal Aveda Institute
HAIR: Jenn Panezich
PHOTO: Tom Carson

The Oak Street Hair Group
HAIR: Karin Perrin
MAKEUP: Celine Russell
PHOTO: Tom Carson

Tangles Salon
HAIR: Robin Cook
MAKEUP: Betty Mekonnen
PHOTO: Tom Carson

Currie Hair Skin & Nail Salon
HAIR: Michele Pritchard-Mckernan
MAKEUP: Jess Moss
PHOTO: Tom Carson

Ladies & Gentlemen
Salon & Spa
HAIR: Michael Pavlick
PHOTO: Tom Carson

Kathy Adams Salon
HAIR: Dalia Ardeu
MAKEUP: Stephanie Adams
PHOTO: Tom Carson

The Oak Street Hair Group
HAIR: Lori Egea
COLOR: Felicia Bellgray
MAKEUP: Celine Russell
PHOTO: Tom Carson

The Ohio Academy
Paul Mitchell Partner School
HAIR: Molly Gooding
MAKEUP: Molly Gooding
PHOTO: Tom Carson

Von Kekel Aveda
Salon Spa
HAIR: Megan Moore
PHOTO: Tom Carson

LONG STYLES

PON International
HAIR: Jamie Queenen
MAKEUP: Jamie Queenen
PHOTO: Taggart
Winterhalter for
Purely Visual

PON International
HAIR: Jamie Queenen
MAKEUP: Jamie Queenen

Currie Hair Skin & Nail Salon
HAIR: Michele Pritchard-Mckernan
MAKEUP: Jess Moss
PHOTO: Tom Carson

Vanis Salon & Day Spa
HAIR: Stephanie Alderson
MAKEUP: Amy Melone
PHOTO: Tom Carson

Claiborne's Salon
HAIR: Claiborne's Design Team
MAKEUP: Claiborne's Design Team
PHOTO: Oma Cain

Salon Solei
HAIR: Tina Reinders
COLOR: Tina Reinders
MAKEUP: Ashlee Gassert
PHOTO: Rita Backus

Von Kekel Aveda Salon Spa
HAIR: Krystal Rodriguez
PHOTO: Tom Carson

Von Kekel Aveda Salon Spa
HAIR: Shawn Von Kekel
PHOTO: Tom Carson

Tangles Salon
HAIR: Robin Cook
MAKEUP: Betty Mckonnen
PHOTO: Tom Carson

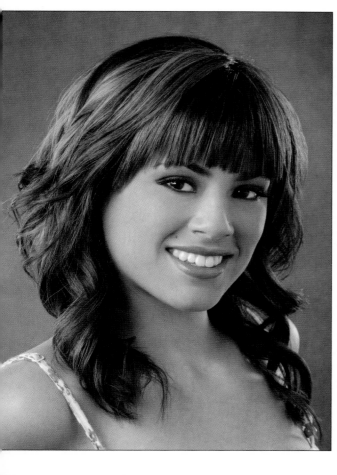

PON International
HAIR: Kaytee Varchetto
MAKEUP: Sara Wayne
PHOTO: Taggart Winterhalter
for Purely Visual

**The Ohio Academy
Paul Mitchell Partner
School**
HAIR: Ashley Henry
MAKEUP: Ashley Henry
PHOTO: Tom Carson

Casal Aveda Institute
HAIR: Nicolette Dovellos
PHOTO: Tom Carson

Sheer Professionals Salon
HAIR: Jennifer Tennant
PHOTO: Tom Carson

Attitudes A Salon
HAIR: Janice Edinger
MAKEUP: Kim Bowers
PHOTO: Tom Carson

The Oak Street Hair Group
HAIR: Lori Egea
MAKEUP: Angela Jones
PHOTO: Tom Carson

LONG STYLES

Casal Aveda Institute
HAIR: Robert Matthews
PHOTO: Tom Carson

Casal Aveda Institute
HAIR: Kalie McElroy
PHOTO: Tom Carson

Casal Aveda Institute
HAIR: Erin Stewart
PHOTO: Tom Carson

Casal Aveda Institute
HAIR: Alyssa Wild
PHOTO: Tom Carson

**Kenneth Shuler
Schools of Cosmetology**
HAIR: Ashley Arrowood
PHOTO: Tom Carson

**The Brown
Aveda Institute**
HAIR: Erin Rolfe
PHOTO: Tom Carson

69

Elizabeth Hurley
PHOTO: Eamonn McCormack
WireImage

70

Diane Lane
PHOTO: Lester Cohen
WireImage

Diane Lane
PHOTO: Jesse Grant
WireImage

Dana Delany
PHOTO: Tony Barson/
WireImage

Jodie Foster
PHOTO: Jon Kopaloff
FilmMagic

Jodie Foster
PHOTO: Robyn Beck
AFP

Marisa Tomei
PHOTO: Charles Eshelman
FilmMagic

Marisa Tomei
PHOTO: Mark Von Holden
WireImage

Heather Locklear
PHOTO: Kevin Parry
WireImage

Heather Locklear
PHOTO: Frederick M. Brown /
Getty Images Entertainment

Valerie Bertinelli
PHOTO: David Livingston
Getty Images
Entertainment

Valerie Bertinelli
PHOTO: Michael Bezjian
WireImage

Cate Blanchett
PHOTO: Jean Baptiste Lacroix
FilmMagic

Cate Blanchett
PHOTO: Eric Ryan
Getty Images Entertainment

Kim Cattrall
PHOTO: Mike Marsland
WireImage

Kim Cattrall
PHOTO: Theo Wargo
WireImage

74

Kelly Preston
PHOTO: Dimitrios
Kambouris
WireImage

Kelly Preston
PHOTO: Jeffrey Mayer
WireImage

Jane Lynch
PHOTO: Lester Cohen
WireImage

Jane Lynch
PHOTO: Frazer Harrison
Getty Images Entertainment

Tea Leoni
PHOTO: Isaac Brekken
Getty Images
Entertainment

Tea Leoni
PHOTO: Shawn Ehlers
WireImage

Diane Keaton
PHOTO: Jemal Countess
WireImage

Diane Keaton
PHOTO: Gregg DeGuire
WireImage

Sela Ward
PHOTO: Dr. Billy Ingram
WireImage

Sela Ward
PHOTO: Lester Cohen
WireImage

Sela Ward
PHOTO: Stefanie Keenan
WireImage

Rene Russo
PHOTO: Neilson Barnard
Getty Images
Entertainment

Rene Russo
PHOTO: John Shearer
WireImage

Naomi Watts
PHOTO: Steve Granitz
WireImage

Naomi Watts
PHOTO: Robyn Beck
AFP

Salon Boucle
HAIR: Mehran
MAKEUP: Jamie Queenin
PHOTO: Taggart Winterhalter
for Purely Visual

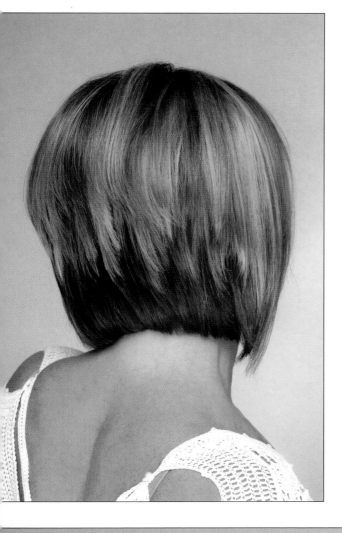

The David Salon
HAIR: Carter
MAKEUP: Ja'Nice Estrada
PHOTO: Taggart
Winterhalter
for Purely Visual

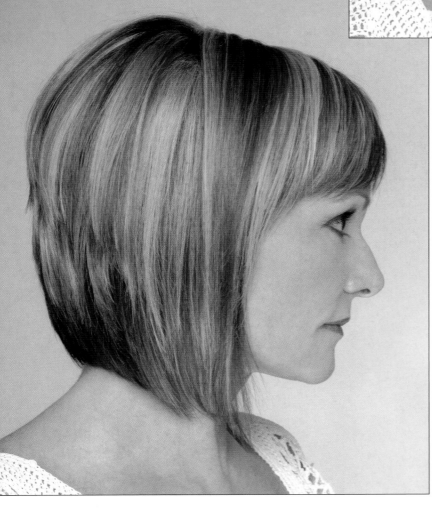

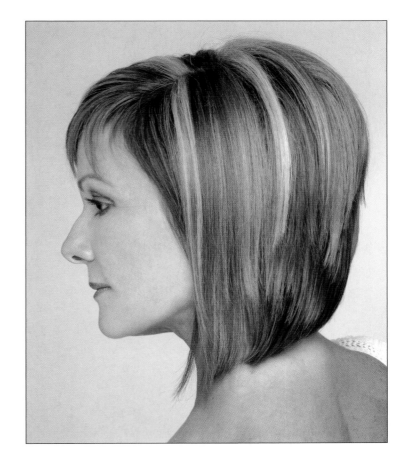

Kathy Adams Salon
HAIR: Kathy McCaffrey
MAKEUP: Felicia Stubbs
PHOTO: Tom Carson

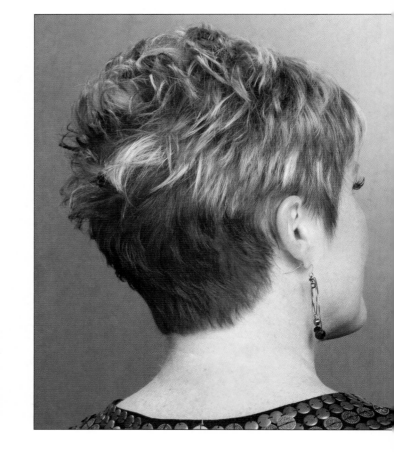

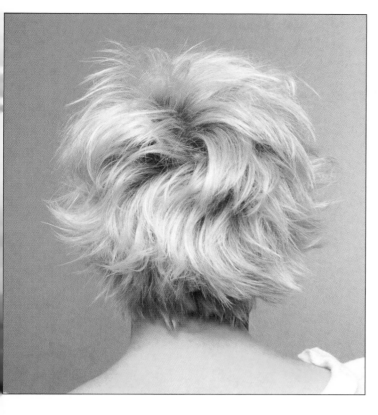

Flux Beauty
HAIR: Angeleah Daidone
MAKEUP: Patricia Daidone
PHOTO: Angeleah Daidone

Anasa Hair Studio
HAIR: Helen Botsis
MAKEUP: Jennifer Foester
PHOTO: Taggart
Winterhalter
for Purely Visual

Anasa Hair Studio
HAIR: Helen Botsis
MAKEUP: Jamie Queenin
PHOTO: Taggart
Winterhalter
for Purely Visual

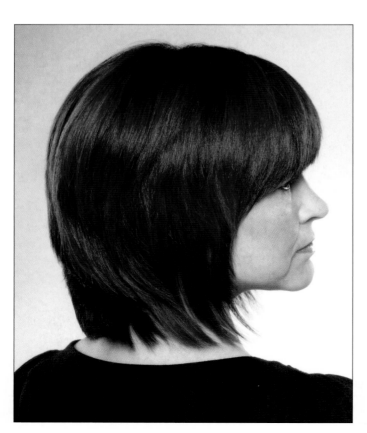

**Argo Hair Company
for Shear Express Inc.**
HAIR: Paige Paxton
COLOR: Paige Paxton
MAKEUP: Paige Paxton
PHOTO: Wendy Reynolds

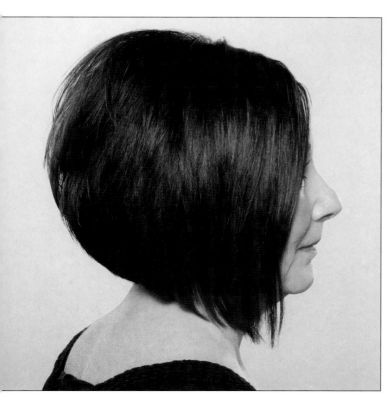

Pavé Nouveau
HAIR: Leann Evans
MAKEUP: Tessa Stull
PHOTO: Taggart
Winterhalter
for Purely Visual

85

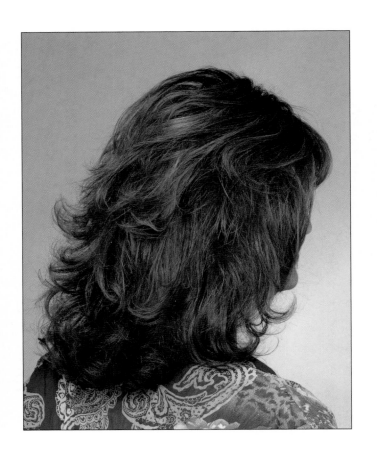

A Carter T. Lund Salon
HAIR: Carter T. Lund
MAKEUP: Ja'Nice Estrada
PHOTO: Taggart Winterhalter
for Purely Visual

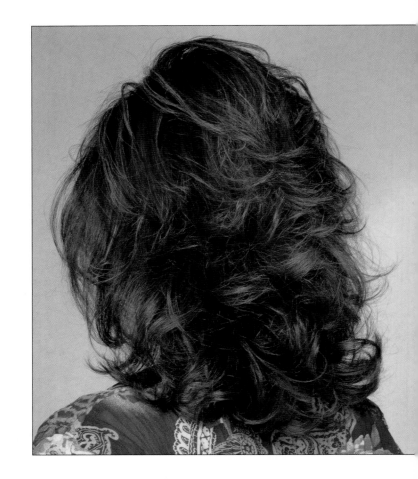

Gadabout Salon
HAIR: Frank Westerberke
PHOTO: Britta Von Uranken

Gadabout Salon
HAIR: Frank Westerberke
PHOTO: Britta Von Uranken

Salon 56
HAIR: Cathy McKinney
MAKEUP: Harold Morris
PHOTO: Taggart Winterhalter
for Purely Visual

Tangles Hair Lounge
HAIR: Kelly Dobbert
MAKEUP: Jamie Queenin
PHOTO: Taggart
Winterhalter
for Purely Visual

Salon 56
HAIR: Jamie Olvera
MAKEUP: Gerine Coronado
PHOTO: Taggart
Winterhalter
for Purely Visual

Pavé Nouveau
HAIR: Carrie Huber
MAKEUP: Jamie Queenin
PHOTO: Taggart
Winterhalter
for Purely Visual

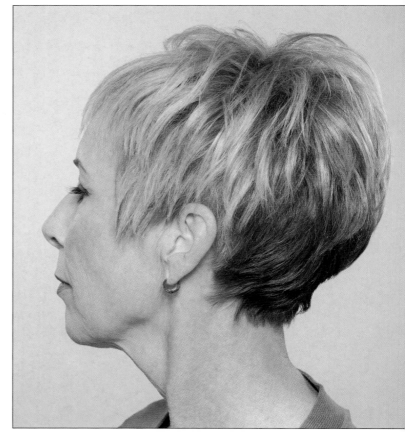

PON International
HAIR: Sara Wayne
MAKEUP: Sara Wayne
PHOTO: Taggart Winterhalter
for Purely Visual

Carter T. Lund and Associates
HAIR: Carter T. Lund
MAKEUP: Jamie Queenin
PHOTO: Taggart Winterhalter
for Purely Visual

Anasa Hair Studio
HAIR: Ashley Lara
MAKEUP: Jamie Queenin
PHOTO: Taggart Winterhalter
for Purely Visual

Edie's Styling Center
HAIR: Rachel Woolums
COLOR: Rachel Woolums
MAKEUP: Lili Casanova
PHOTO: Scott Bryant
Art direction by Larry Oskin
& The Marketing
Solutions Team

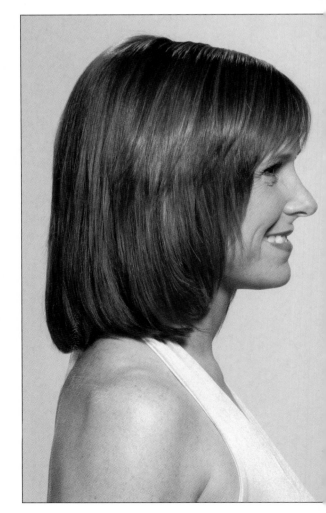

Salon Solei
HAIR: Tina Reinders
COLOR: Tina Reinders
MAKEUP: Ashlee Gassert
PHOTO: Rita Backus

Attitudes A Salon
HAIR: Janice Edinger
MAKEUP: Kim Bowers
PHOTO: Tom Carson

INSPIRE INDEX VOLUME SEVENTY SEVEN

HAIR FASHION FOR SALON CLIENTS

Publisher/CEO: Deborah Carver • Managing Director: Sheryl Lenzkes • Art Director: Michael Block
To Contact Us: Creative Age Communications • 7628 Densmore Avenue, Van Nuys, California 91406-2042 • PH 800.634.8500 • FAX 818.782.7450
Interested in getting published . . . go to inspirebooks.com to download submission forms and information